KEY PATTERNS AND ANIMALS

A Celtic Art Workbook

DEDICATION
To the Celtic spirit and the works of Françoise Henry,
George Bain, J. Romilly Allen and the inspirers and
masters of the past.

A man in the jaws of a beast. From St Mark's Gospel,
Book of Kells, ninth century AD.

Title-page
A cross carpet page from an early eighth-century gospel-book,
formerly at Schloss Hamburg in Germany.

Copyright page
An eighth-century key pattern centre from a design on a cross-slab at Rosemarkie,
Ross-shire, in Scotland. The key border comes from the Book of Durrow,
which dates from the seventh century AD.

Contents page
An adaptation of a portrait of St Mark from the ninth-century Book of Kells.

KEY PATTERNS AND ANIMALS

A Celtic Art Workbook

COURTNEY DAVIS

BLANDFORD

ACKNOWLEDGEMENTS

My grateful thanks to Laurence Stroud, who worked with me on the text and who is always a great friend and an inspiration in my life and work. Thanks also to all the great souls I have met in the past twenty years on my Celtic quest, who have befriended and encouraged me onwards both in this world and the otherworld. Long may all their lights shine.

First published in the United Kingdom in 1999 by Blandford
Reprinted 2000

Copyright pictures and text © 1999 Courtney Davis
Copyright design and layout © Blandford

Distributed in the United States by Sterling Publishing Co., Inc., 387 Park Avenue South, New York, NY 10016–8810

A Cataloguing-in-Publication Data entry for this title is available from the British Library

ISBN 0-7137-2744-6

Text design Richard Carr
Printed and bound in Great Britain by Hillman Printers (Frome) Ltd, Somerset

Blandford
Illustrated Division
The Orion Publishing Group
Wellington House
125 Strand
London WC2R OBB

CONTENTS

Foreword 6

Introduction 7

Key Patterns 11

Zoomorphic Patterns 25

Further Reading 63

Index 64

foreword

This design is adapted from a gold mount found at the Sutton Hoo ship burial, dated around AD 625. See colour picture 2 for some colouring ideas.

ALFRED AIKEN wrote in the Preface to his book *That Which Is*: 'It is not a book intended to be read at a single sitting.' So, too, with Courtney Davis's art workbooks; they will best be 'understood and felt' by repeating the experience over and over again. Each time the feeling and colours will be different as your thoughts vary. You will understand the subtle energies that the Celts would have recognized within themselves as they drew their key patterns and zoomorphic illustrations. Life is a tremendously rich and fluid tapestry, full of shapes and colours that alter almost by the minute as our thoughts perceive moods and ideas.

Courtney has once again provided us with an opportunity to search into our hidden consciousness. Again he has provided us with insights that can help us to realize our inner being by encouraging us to paint pictures with the imagination that only we, as the individual, can perceive. If you are a budding artist, this book will encourage you to achieve greater things. If you are inclined to use colour for healing, you will find your mind searching for the elusive colour shading to give your pictures the expression that brings a subtle healing energy to those who require healing qualities. Courtney has used his techniques of healing and the ability to understand the inner being in his works from the very beginning.

Throughout the years that my wife Beatrice and I have known Courtney, we have seen 'patterns of change' enter into his personal life. Like the pictures that he has created for you, some 'patterns of change' are difficult and complex. Each key pattern and each zoomorphic illustration is also an expression of life in one form or another.

To those of you who simply want to practise drawing and colouring Celtic art in your leisure time you will not be disappointed, for there are so many different designs to appreciate with both the key patterns and the zoomorphic illustrations that Courtney has provided. Whatever your intention, either to help find an inner enlightenment or just to colour and find satisfaction in the colouring alone, you can contemplate the art of the Celtic past and, as Courtney would say, 'acknowledge the *source*'.

Laurence H. Stroud,
Polgooth, Cornwall

INTRODUCTION

THE SOURCES for much of the material in this book come from my own adaptations, over the years, of the designs in illuminated pages from Celtic manuscripts, jewellery and the carvings from the various stone crosses found in Ireland, Scotland, England and Wales. These sources include the seventh-century Lindisfarne Gospels, the magnificent ninth-century Book of Kells, the Sutton Hoo ship burial and the Houelt cross-slab in Wales. I have built up other designs purely from rough doodles, constantly worked on until they become complete.

The artists of the illuminated manuscripts were monks, who worked in scriptoriums, and they were highly valued as craftsmen. They used a variety of brushes for the decoration, probably made from marten fur, as well as quills from swans, geese, crows and other birds. Knives were used to scrape mistakes from the vellum.

Celtic design was mainly abstract, with swirling spirals, key patterns and knotwork but zoomorphic (animal) and anthropomorphic (humanoid) designs were also used, interlaced in complex shapes. Among the detail on the Chi-Rho page (*chi* and *rho* are the first two Greek letters of 'Christ') of the Book of Kells, for example, are faces and two cats watching two mice.

The symbols in Celtic art have a potent power, and they have been used by people for thousands of years - pagan symbols were later absorbed into Christian art. These symbols are still as powerful and relevant to those of us working with them today as they were to people in the past. They are reflections of both the natural world and the otherworld - of which we are all a part - and the movement of their unseen energies affects all of us. These subtle energies can be sensed and utilized by healers and dowsers; indeed, I often feel 'sparks of light' guiding my own pen or brush as I work.

In the Foreword to one of my previous volumes, *The Celtic Art Source Book*, Johan Quanjer wrote:

When we experience the symbol as the gateway to higher thinking and living, we become aware that we have transcended the personality and touched deeply on our soul quality. We then recognize that it is through the self or soul that we make an inner contact with the godhead, on a level beyond reason or intellect. Furthermore we accept that we are part of the whole and that the whole is part of us. By this touch of the soul we are harmonized, vivified and recharged with energy. We are imbued with the certainty of the saint and the faith of the Apostle and are so renewed and ready to go back to the area of our personal lives and meet any of its emergencies and challenges with courage and joy.

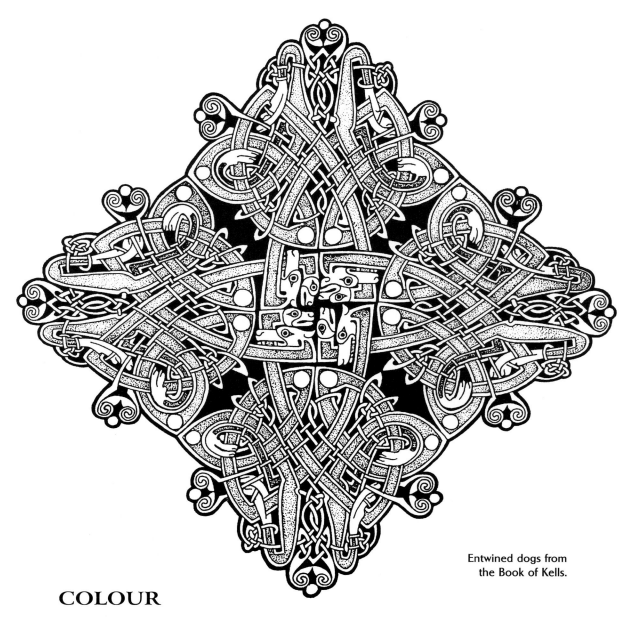

Entwined dogs from
the Book of Kells.

COLOUR

Colour plays a very important part in our lives. In the fashion world, for example, designers obviously know that different people favour specific colours while other colours may not suit them. Colour choice also changes with the seasons. Indeed, people may believe that a particular colour brings them bad luck or drains their energy while other colours make them feel joyful and full of life. Colour affects our mood and our surroundings. The way we use colour to decorate our homes reflects our personality. We may prefer 'warm' colours or 'cool' colours, and use harmonizing colours or perhaps contrasting colours for a special effect.

Through the ages colour has also been used in symbolic ways, such as green representing nature, growth and fertility. The colours used by the Celtic illuminators reflected the mystical, jewel-like quality of their great works. The

pigments came from various sources, including plants, animals and minerals. Bede, the theologian and historian (*c.* 673–735) praised the colours prepared in Ireland, especially the permanence and brilliance of the red made from whelks.

Bernard Meehan, in *The Book of Kells*, tells us that the illuminators of the eighth-century Lichfield Gospels and the ninth-century Book of Kells employed an unusual colouristic technique, which involved adding a thin, translucent wash of one colour on top of another to give a relief effect. Sometimes as many as three pigments were painted on top of a ground layer. This relief effect has now been largely lost because, during the nineteenth century, the pages of the gospel-books were wetted so that they could be flattened.

Today, we have the versatility of modern colours. In the colour pictures in this book I have used Sky Blue, Brilliant Blue, Process Cyan, Permanent Green, Bengal Rose, Primary Red, Lemon Yellow and Cadmium Yellow Pale. I am sure the Celtic illuminators would have enormously enjoyed the wide range of colours we now have, as well as all the modern art tools and techniques. Nevertheless, with the limitations of their time, they still produced stunning and magical images that continue to enthral us at the end of the twentieth century.

USING THE BOOK

Like its companion volume, *Knotwork and Spirals*, this is meant to be a practical book. The illustrations are especially designed for people of all ages to adapt and colour. I suggest that, when you have chosen a picture to paint, instead of colouring it in the book you should photocopy it, either larger or reduced - whichever suits you. You could also copy the patterns freehand or trace them, adding or discarding parts from various pages until you eventually have your own unique picture. You can even cut and paste pictures, or parts of pictures, together.

For drawing and colouring you could use felt-tip pens, pencil, ink, gouache, watercolour or even embroidery thread. I always use gouache in my work because I create the detail in my pictures as I go along and this medium gives me the ability to cover over one colour with another when I need to make changes. You can also use a variety of papers and card on which to create your designs - perhaps textured or vellum paper might be suitable for a special effect.

Some people like to use grids to plan out their work, but personally I do not use them although I have included in this book some illustrations that may help to give a general idea of the way the constructions of the patterns in my work are built up. Many people who have tried and failed with the

system of grids, and therefore have been put off persevering with the patterns, contact me. There are a number of very helpful books (see Further Reading, p. 63) that deal with the methods of constructing the patterns. I always suggest to people who are having trouble that they should put aside the books if they feel that they hinder their personal artistic spirit. In this case, you should just play with the lines until an overall pleasing pattern is formed. Then you can spend time refining your work. Once you have got to grips with the general idea of the rhythm of the patterns you can return to the books if you need to, and continue with a greater understanding of the mechanics of this particular art form.

What colours should you use? I suggest that you should experiment. Personally, I never pre-plan the colours of my paintings; I always let the picture lead its own way. The colour examples in this book are meant as a guide only; if you like a certain combination of colours you could perhaps adapt them for use in another picture. I like to experiment constantly. Sometimes you will find that the colours do not work out satisfactorily, but you should just persevere with another combination. On the other hand, when an unusual combination is successful it is really uplifting. Practise using different colour combinations, and don't tie yourself to rigid colour schemes.

You could also use a sponge or a toothbrush to lay on a background colour, giving the effect of stone or wood, and then superimpose a design on top. Images such as colour picture 1, because it is fairly simple, could be worked in this way.

I hope you find the book fun and interesting as well as a challenge. Remember to let your own artistic spirit come forward, and don't worry if your first pictures are a disappointment. Just keep trying and let your pen and brush, or other medium, flow naturally. You will be surprised and excited by the results. Good luck!

A step border from the seventh-century Book of Durrow.

key patterns

A pattern taken from a panel in the Book of Durrow.

THE TERM key pattern is used to describe this particular ornament because of its resemblance to the perforations on a key which allows it to turn a lock. Patterns similar to the Celtic style of ornament have a long history of use as decoration in various parts of the world. Square and diagonal key patterns have been found, for instance, in Russia; they include a series of interlocking swastikas engraved on mammoth ivory dating back to 20,000-15,000 years BC. These are panelled in a similar fashion to key patterns on various carved standing stones from Durham in England to Caithness in Scotland and Penmon in Anglesey, Wales, and were later to be seen in illuminated manuscripts.

Key patterns arrived in Britain centuries before the Romans. The difference in the close association between the Celtic key pattern and the Greek fret pattern lies in the bending of the links, at certain points, at angles of 45 degrees instead of 90 degrees.

Key patterns are really spirals in straight lines. When connected, they become a processional path leading through a complex labyrinth to the still centre. It is a journey through progressive levels of experience - physical, mental and spiritual. At ancient religious festivals, the adept would step barefoot into a labyrinth that had been cut into the ground. They would begin the sacred dance, moving in a clockwise direction in deep contemplation, absorbing the earth's energies. With every step taken, and obstacle overcome, was a reawakening to a greater knowledge. Finally, they reached the sacred omphalos, the point where heaven and earth are joined at the very centre of the labyrinth. This journey of devotion was the equivalent of a pilgrimage to Jerusalem for the later Christians.

I have also included some step patterns in this section which belong to a European prehistoric past. In his book *Celtic Art in Pagan and Christian Times* J. Romilly Allen thought that these might have had a textile origin, perhaps copied from woven belts or other fabrics. Step patterns are used to great effect on enamelled metalwork, such as the finds from the Sutton Hoo ship burial and on the carpet pages in the Lindisfarne Gospels (AD 698).

Françoise Henry, in her book *Irish Art in the Early Christian Period to 800 AD* suggests that key and step patterns may have a 'solar connotation, being sometimes associated with fire and

The Houelt cross-slab, Llantwit Major, South Glamorgan, Wales, ninth century AD.

At the top left of the page is a sample of the grid system (a) used by many Celtic artists for creating key patterns. Rather than try to grid out the entire picture you want to create, split the border or panel into equal portions and then draw out one section to size so that it fits, as shown by b, c, d and e. Then you can begin filling in the picture by tracing and repeating one section to another over and over until your panel or border is complete. Make sure the sections link up properly and remember to save space to square off the work at the end.

then perhaps with the spirit'. Even though the exact meaning of these patterns is now lost, she thinks there can be little doubt that spiral, interlacing and step patterns, and stylized foliage, were never mere ornaments. For centuries all of them had been carefully spread over objects and on the surface of walls for the sake of their protective virtues and hidden symbols.

In *Celtic Art, Methods of Construction* George Bain explains that both the labyrinth or maze and the meander symbols influenced the design of the key patterns of the Pictish school of Celtic art and that labyrinth designs can be found in the Books of Durrow and Kells as well as the Lindisfarne Gospels. One excellent example that he points out is an ornamented stone with a labyrinth design in the National Museum in Dublin.

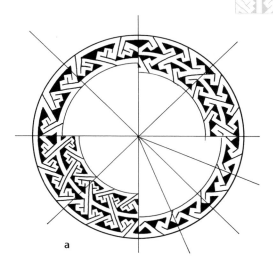

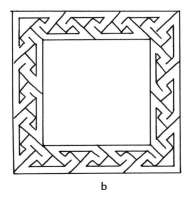

a   b

These two patterns were produced in the same way as the ones shown opposite. Cut the circle (a) into sections and fit in the pattern so that it can follow on to the next segment. I personally do not work on a grid system but copy roughly and redraw until the template is evenly balanced. By using this method, if you make a small mistake in your measurements when you are tracing the border, you can stretch it or shorten it slightly without too much bother. The wider the pattern the narrower it is as it gets closer to the middle, so always remember to take that into account when planning the design. It is a good idea to work with a larger segment for a deeper border.

The border of the square (b) has very simple mitred corners. Some of the wider borders become very complex and can lead to a lot of frustration when you are trying to work with them. As well as my own books, there are many other source books available that contain samples of key patterns and these are very useful references to work from when planning out the overall pattern of your own design.

A step pattern from the seventh-century Lindisfarne Gospels. In colour picture 1 I have used a variety of colours to fill the panels, plus shadow lines.

The empty boxes in the pattern could be filled by a variety of designs. Some ideas can be found in other pictures, such as those on pages 6 and 17.

Try and experiment with one overall colour in different strengths and, with some panels,
just a hint of another colour mixed in.

These step patterns are excellent for quilting projects.

In colour picture 3 the swastika boxes in each corner are very simple. They could be adapted by creating a chequered pattern within the step design.

This pattern originated from the Nigg stone, Ross-shire, Scotland, eighth to ninth century AD.
This pattern would work well printed on to fabric.

In colour picture 4 I used light green and blue in the pattern around the edge of the picture.
You could try a much darker blue or a purple combination instead, with a lighter centre.

I always enjoy using a rainbow effect in my pictures, and this works well with a design like the one above. In colour picture 5 the rainbow hues bring the simple image alive.

This image comes from a variety of ninth-century sources. A colour idea might be a fiery sun at the centre, with golden spokes as its rays and a blue outer ring.

This design is from the Pen-Arthur cross-slab in Pembrokeshire, Wales. After masking the picture, the background to this image could be sponged or flecked to create a stone effect.

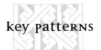

An eighth-century key pattern from the design on a cross-slab at Rosemarkie, Ross-shire, Scotland.
By painting a deeper colour to the key-pattern edge than I have created in colour picture 6 you
might make a stronger frame for the lighter centre.

This picture is adapted from the seventh-century tombstone of St Berechtir at Tullease, Co. Cork, in Ireland. In colour picture 7 I have used a variety of colours - perhaps just two to three colours might make it an even more striking picture.

ZOOMORPHIC patterns

ZOOMORPHIC ORNAMENTS are those based on animals, birds and reptiles. Anthropomorphic ornaments are those based on the human body. Both of these make an early appearance in the art of Bronze Age Britain and Ireland, and in European forms of Celtic art. Zoomorphic and anthropomorphic ornament shows us that nothing is as it seems: winding tails turn into the branches of a plant; cats and dogs have bird bodies, and so on. Craftsmen fashioned them into a complex contortion of bodies that still somehow conformed to nature.

Many of the pre-Christian gods were depicted with bird or animal parts. Shape-changing was said to have been practised by the druids and their gods in early legends, and by semi-mythological characters who adopted an animal form. It is said that St Patrick was able to shape-change, at one time turning into a stag to escape capture by pagan warriors.

The gospel-books often used zoomorphic ornament in their carpet pages, panels and initials. Fine examples include the Books of Durrow and Armagh, the Lindisfarne Gospels and the Macdurnan Gospels. It is in the Book of Kells that such art reaches its heights; the explosion of detail on its pages and the intricacy of the workmanship is a lasting reminder of the mastery and imagination of the illuminators. In the Book of Kells Christ was identified and accompanied by a large number of different symbols, including the fish (the earliest Christian symbol for Christ and wisdom), the lion (the symbol of resurrection), the snake (another symbol of resurrection because of the belief that it regains its youth when it sheds its skin) and the peacock (symbol of incorruptibility because, according to ancient belief, its flesh is so hard that it does not putrefy).

Every winged being is symbolic of spirituality. According to Jung, the bird is a beneficent animal representing spirits or angels and the souls of the faithful. It is thought that the birds of the Lindisfarne Gospels, painted by Eadfrith, may be cormorants, inspired by the rich wildlife that surrounds Lindisfarne or Holy Island, off the coast of Northumberland. Dogs are an emblem of faithfulness, and in Christian symbolism they have the function of the sheepdog, guarding and guiding the flock and therefore at times becoming a symbol of the priest.

In the Introduction to my book *Celtic Beasts* Dennis O'Neill and I have written:

The Celtic dog design was created by simple doodling and stretching the body until it felt balanced.

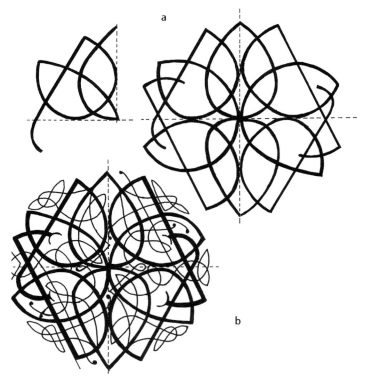

The Celts were a people deeply connected with creation. Animals were a constant part of Celtic life, both literally and symbolically. To this day in Ireland, if a bird happens to fly into the house, this can portend good luck. In the same way, if a frog hops into the house, it can mean that someone is about to die. Similarly, in the Scottish Highlands small birds are often considered harbingers of death.

The Celts not only relied on animals for their survival but they respected them, learned from them, and honoured them. They decorated their jewellery, weapons, monuments, and, in the Christian period, their manuscripts, book covers, reliquaries, and chapels, with brilliant, intricate, elaborate zoomorphic designs.

I re-created this design from the Book of Kells in a couple of rough layouts (a). These led to the semi-finished design (b). In the next stage I would start to add ornament and, finally, colouring to the image.

In *The Book of Kells,* by Sir Edward Sullivan, the author tells us that many pagan elements, including the adoption of the serpentine form by the Church for decorative purposes, were absorbed into the practices of the Christian missionaries and afterwards became permanently interwoven with Christian belief. Both St Jerome and St Augustine strongly upheld this course of action on the grounds of expediency when dealing with converts from paganism.

Dennis O'Neill and I go on to say in *Celtic Beasts*:

In order to enter the world of Celtic beasts it is essential to set aside all linear thinking. To understand the role of animals in the ancient myths and in the lives of the saints, it will be necessary to see them as more than either simple beasts or archetypal symbols. We are about to make a journey along a spiritual path, the origin of which can be traced to the earliest remaining evidence of human worship. Since archeologists have claimed that the bear is the oldest identifiable deity, we will begin with her.

There is a thread which forms a connecting link, running all the way back to the ancient Bear Mother and forward into Christian hagiography. That thread is shamanism.

Finally, Johan Quanjer says, in his Foreword to my volume *The Celtic Art Source Book*:

> *The symbol has no power of its own; it is only what it represents that exerts an influence. We should not be forever bound to it, for once we have begun to become self-actualized individuals the need for symbolism will disappear. However, if we remove symbols before we have risen in consciousness, we may cut ourselves off from that source which enables us to achieve cosmic awareness.*

These are two rough drafts (a) that I used to build up the final border panel (b)
from my book *St Patrick: A Visual Celebration*.

This design is from the eighth-century Lichfield Gospels, also known as the Book of Chad.
The illuminator was probably inspired by the earlier Lindisfarne Gospels as there are similarities in
technique and colouring; a delicate shade of lilac was used while the bodies of the dogs were
painted red against a black background.

This picture is an adaptation from a panel in the seventh-century Lindisfarne Gospels.
This design could easily be adapted by joining another three sections from the necks of the
dogs to make a larger panel.

Much of the elaborate zoomorphic art in the illuminated gospel-books was focused on the dog and the bird. The nose or the beak of these creatures, as depicted by the Northumbrian schools, tended to be longer than those in the work created by the Irish illuminators.

This design could be further enhanced with a knotwork outer band similar to
that in colour picture 15.

A detail taken from the Lindisfarne Gospels. The page was decorated in red, green, blue, lilac and yellow against a black background. The necks at the top and bottom could be stretched to fit a larger panel.

1

2

3

4

5

6

7

8

9

10

11

12

13

14

15

16

This pattern could be squared up and then joined to another three copies, with the knotwork from the head and tail linking up the panel. Perhaps each section could be alternately light and dark.

This is part of the illumination for the Chi-Rho from the twelfth-century Harley MS 1802 in the British Library, London. Influenced by the illuminated books from Europe, the knotwork in the manuscripts at this date ceased to be a continuous thread and was instead turned into foliage. Spirals, which were the first patternwork used by the Celtic illuminators, had been discarded long before. Colour picture 8 shows the vitality you can achieve by painting.

This picture is actually two triangular sections from the Lindisfarne Gospels put together. However, they were never properly connected — try linking them up by the head and tail threads.

In colour picture 9 I used blues and greens in the picture, with yellow knotwork. You could add more detail to your picture by filling in the serpents' bodies with dots and scales.

This picture contains sections that have not been linked up. The threads can be easily joined, and you could also try extending and bending the toes of the birds at the bottom and the top so that they overlap each other.

More detail could be added to this serpent picture; thin inner bands could follow the edge of the bodies with diamonds and dots added to the centre. Be careful at the corners when filling the bodies with a pattern. A good tip is to do anything that might cause a problem on the very tight bends first and then work back.

This picture comes from part of a cross panel in the Lichfield Gospels. In the original very little colour and detail are used. In colour picture 10 I probably used only four basic hues, which I then mixed to harmonize the overall colours of the picture. Feathers could be added to the birds' backs and necks for more detail.

This design originates from a panel in the Book of Kells. In colour picture 11 the light and dark tones of the background are graduated; this effect can give the picture another dimension. This pattern can easily be adapted so that it is joined to more sections of the same, thereby creating a carpet design.

The base of the entwined dog, if adapted, could become one arm of a cross design, or stretched wide to fill a panel.

The Tree of Life was initially a pagan symbol that was later adapted by the Christian scribes. Its use was a religious one and not merely decorative.

This adapted picture comes from a panel in the Book of Kells in which the serpents were coloured in alternating blue and cream pigments, with a black background. I rearranged the movement of the serpents so that they are interlocked. This means that the colour of one serpent will entwine with another which, I hope, will make a more interesting picture to paint.

In colour picture 12 I used Bengal Rose in different shades to colour the serpents. To make the pattern even more interesting the colour used for each serpent could be darker at the tail and could get gradually lighter as it reaches the head.

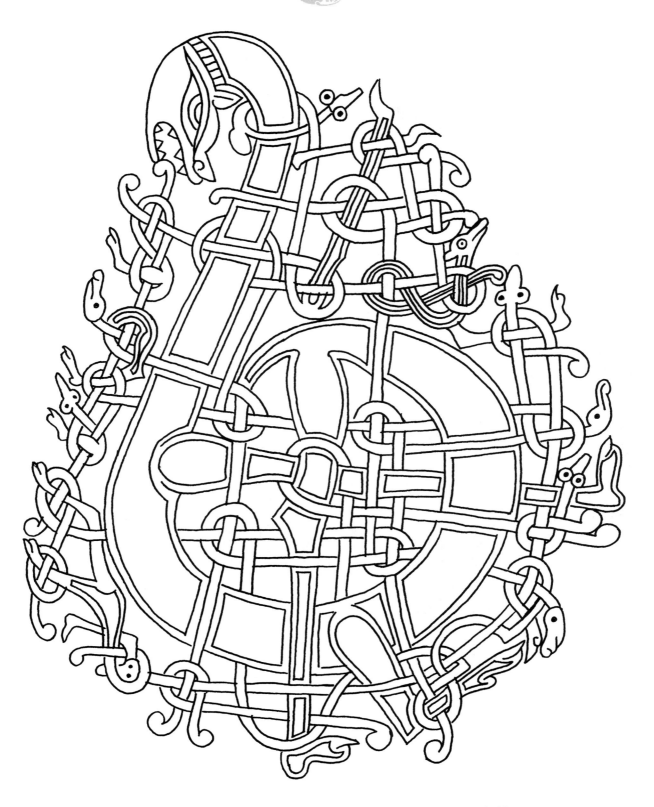

This initial is taken from the twelfth-century Couper Angus Psalter, which was probably written in Bangor, Ireland. The artistic skill of the illuminator is inferior to the earlier eighth- and ninth-century manuscripts of the golden age of Celtic illumination, though the artist may well have studied them.

The letters RIN from '(P)RIN(CIPIO)', the opening word from St John's Gospel in the Book of Kells.
The size of the original is 3.75 x 1.87 cm (1 $^1/_2$ x $^3/_4$ in).

The initial G from the Book of Kells. In colour picture 13 I have added additional ornament and put a shadow line around the body of the dogs to take some flatness off the initial.

An initial adapted from the eleventh-century MS Rawlinson B502 in the British Library. Books like this and the Book of Dun Cow were produced to preserve the writings of epics, poems and genealogies left after the ravages of the Vikings, who had destroyed many of the earlier works.

The Book of Kells uses the serpent symbol more than any other and serpents are frequently shown with duck-like heads and fish tails. The serpent symbolizes Christ's resurrection, because of its ability to regain its youth by shedding its skin.

Do not be afraid to experiment with colour. Most of the time I do not have a fixed idea of the colours I am going to work with and try to let the picture create itself. This image comes originally from a fragment of 426–427 Codex 1395 in the British Library, dating from the eighth century. Colour picture 14 shows the brilliant jewel-like quality achieved by painting.

I am always amazed at the imagination and skill of the Celtic monks who illuminated the gospel-books. This is part of a panel from the Lichfield Gospels. Panels such as this have inspired many of my own works over the years.

The body of the dog could be broken up into sections with different types of ornament, such as a chequered pattern, diamond shapes, or scales and dots, to give it more detail. You could also pick out the backgrounds to certain knot sections and give them a different colour.

Another complex panel adapted from the Lindisfarne Gospels. The main colours in the original
are lilac, blue and an orange/yellow. It is easy to get lost when creating these patterns and
I often find that by using tracing paper I can build up an overlay of the picture and see where
the pattern is going.

A detail taken from the Book of Kells (the original is 3.4 cm /1¹/₃in diameter).

The late seventh-century Durham Gospels is thought to have been produced at the scriptorium on Lindisfarne, and the dogs shown here come from an initial in St John's Gospel. Much of this gospel-book is missing or damaged but it is thought that it might have been originally as rich in decoration as the slightly earlier Lindisfarne Gospels. Colour picture 15 shows the extra definition you can achieve by colouring the bodies, border and background with harmonizing or contrasting hues.

The idea for this picture came initially from the Book of Kells. I adapted it heavily and it now looks very different from the original. Don't worry about copying pictures — it is a good exercise. You can create your own designs by, at first, starting to alter small sections before going on to major reconstruction.

This picture was built up from a triangular section in the Book of Kells. It is often helpful to do tracing overlays so you can see the possibility of the finished picture and then spend time — and a great deal of patience — working out the overlapping details.

This pattern is almost the same as that on page 51 but here it is altered into a circle. This design originated from the Lichfield Gospels.

This is a panel, doubled up, from the Lindisfarne Gospels. In colour picture 16 each dog is a different colour, thereby creating a rainbow effect.

An initial from the Southampton Psalter, dating from between the late tenth and early eleventh centuries. It could be adapted to sit on top of a panel, its body forming a border to the work. When you see these designs always keep a look-out for the potential to adapt them for future projects.

This picture was created from a triangular section in the Book of Kells. It was linked together with two more sections and then bent to fit a circle. The heads of the serpents could be twisted so that they bite into the outer border of the disc.

Matthew, Mark, Luke and John were depicted in the Gospels by four symbols - man, lion, calf and eagle - from the Book of Revelations. The symbols together form the symbol of Christ himself.

further reading

BOOKS BY COURTNEY DAVIS

The Art of Celtia, Blandford, 1994.

Celtic Art of Courtney Davis, Spirit of Celtia, 1985.

The Celtic Art Source Book, Blandford, 1985.

Celtic Beasts, Blandford, 1999.

Celtic Borders and Decoration, Blandford, 1992.

Celtic Design and Motifs, Dover, 1991.

Celtic Illumination: *The Irish School*, Thames and Hudson, 1998.

Celtic Image, Blandford, 1996.

Celtic Initials and Alphabets, Blandford, 1997.

The Celtic Mandala Book, Blandford, 1993

Celtic Ornament: Art of the Scribe, Blandford, 1996.

The Celtic Saint Book, Blandford, 1995.

The Celtic Tarot, Aquarian, 1990.

King Arthur's Return, Blandford, 1995.

Knotwork and Spirals: *A Celtic Art Workbook*, Blandford, 1999.

St Patrick: A Visual Celebration, Blandford, 1998.

A Treasury of Celtic Designs, Constable, 1998.

You can view the art of Courtney Davis on his web site: www.celtic-art.com

OTHER BOOKS OF INTEREST

Allen, J. Romilly, *Celtic Art in Pagan and Christian Times*, Bracken Books, 1993.

Bain, George, *Celtic Art: Methods of Construction*, Constable, 1951.

Bain, Ian, *Celtic Knotwork*, Constable, 1986.

Bryce, Derek, *Symbolism of the Cross*, Llanerch Enterprises, 1989.

Meehan, Bernard, *The Book of Kells*, Thames and Hudson, 1994.

Zaczek, Iain, *Celtic Design: A Sourcebook of Patterns and Motifs*,
   Studio Editions, 1995.

An initial from the Southampton Psalter.

INDEX

Berechtir, St, tombstone 24
border panels, construction
   of 27

carpet designs 2, 11
Chad, Book of *see* Lichfield
   Gospels
Chi-Rho pages 7, 34
colour, using 8–9, 10, 15, 21,
   23, 43, 44
   background 10, 40
   combinations 19
   contrasting 8, 55
   harmonizing 8, 39, 55
   rainbow effect 20, 59
   symbolism 8

diamonds, creating 38, 52
dots, using 36, 52
Dun Cow, Book of 48
Durham Gospels 55
Durrow, Book of 2, 10, 11, 12

foliage, stylized 12, 34
426–427 Codex 1395 50
felt-tip pens 9

gouache 9
grids 9–10, 12, 13

Harley MS 1802 34
Houelt cross-slab, Wales 7, 11

illuminators 8, 28, 30
initials 45, 47, 48, 60, 63
ink 9

Kells, Book of 2, 7, 8, 12,
   40, 43, 46, 47, 49, 54,
   56, 57, 61, 64

Lichfield Gospels 28, 39, 51,
   58
Lindisfarne Gospels 7, 11,
   12, 13, 28, 29, 32, 35,
   53, 55, 59

manuscripts, Celtic 7, 11, 26
MS Rawlinson B502 48

Nigg stone, Scotland 18

paper
   textured 9
   vellum 9
patterns
   anthropomorphic 7, 25
   chequered 17, 52

construction of 10, 12, 13
key 7, 11–24
   diagonal 11
   square 11
   step 11, 13, 16, 17
knotwork 7, 31, 33
spiral 7, 34
zoomorphic 7, 25–62
   birds 25, 30, 37
   dogs 25, 29, 30, 41, 47,
      52
   serpents 36, 38, 43, 44,
      49,61
Pen-Arthur cross-slab, Wales
22

Rosemarkie cross-slab,
   Scotland 2, 23

sacred dance, the 11
shape-changing 25
Southampton Psalter 63
Sutton Hoo ship burial 6, 11
symbols, animal 25, 49, 62

tracing paper, using 9, 53,57
Tree of Life 42

watercolour 9

This design is taken from the Book of Kells.